Wolf Hill

Ghost
Najma's Story

Roderick Hunt
Illustrated by Alex Brychta

OXFORD
UNIVERSITY PRESS

OXFORD
UNIVERSITY PRESS

Great Clarendon Street, Oxford OX2 6DP

Oxford University Press is a department of the University of Oxford.
It furthers the University's objective of excellence in research, scholarship,
and education by publishing worldwide in

Oxford   New York

Auckland   Cape Town   Dar es Salaam   Hong Kong   Karachi
Kuala Lumpur   Madrid   Melbourne   Mexico City   Nairobi
New Delhi   Shanghai   Taipei   Toronto

With offices in

Argentina   Austria   Brazil   Chile   Czech Republic   France   Greece
Guatemala   Hungary   Italy   Japan   Poland   Portugal   Singapore
South Korea   Switzerland   Thailand   Turkey   Ukraine   Vietnam

Oxford is a registered trade mark of Oxford University Press
in the UK and in certain other countries

British Library Cataloguing in Publication Data

Data available

ISBN   978 0 19 918748 5

20   19   18

Printed in China

Paper used in the production of this book is a natural, recyclable product
made from wood grown in sustainable forests. The manufacturing process
conforms to the environmental regulations of the country of origin.

Chapter 1

Najma felt nervous. She looked out through the window. The bus was driving away through the tall iron gates. She had a sick feeling in her tummy.

Three nights away from home seemed a long time.

Najma looked at Gizmo and Andy. Gizmo's glasses looked misty. Andy was blinking a lot. It was their first big school trip. She guessed that they felt nervous, too.

Najma had never been in such a big house before. It smelled of polish and dusty old books. On the walls were big paintings in heavy gold frames.

A picture of a girl caught her eye. The girl was about ten years old. She was wearing a white dress. Over it, she wore a long blue cloak with a hood. The cloak hung in soft folds, almost to the ground. The girl's face was very pale.

Najma just couldn't take her eyes off the picture. The girl looked so sad.

Then she heard Kat's voice. 'Are you all right, Najma?' she asked. 'We've got to go into the hallway. Mr Saffrey wants us. Didn't you hear him call?'

'Sorry,' said Najma. 'I was miles away.'

'We've got to find our bedrooms,' said Kat. 'I expect you, me and Loz will be together.'

'Of course we will,' Najma said.

Chapter 2

The hallway had a huge staircase. Mr Saffrey stood on the third stair. He looked down and smiled at everyone.

'Here we are at Cranley Manor,' he said. 'I expect you are all very excited. It's a wonderful place for our school trip. But the first job is to find our bedrooms. Mrs Scott will tell you where you are sleeping.'

Mrs Scott had a list. 'Most bedrooms have four beds, but some have two,' she said. 'I've done my best to put you with your friends. But I can't suit everyone.'

She began to read out a list. She got to Kat and Loz. 'I've put you in a room with two beds,' she said. 'Najma, Jamie-Lee, Lucy and Emma will be in a room with four beds.'

Najma couldn't believe it. She felt tears sting her eyes. She hated the idea of sharing a room with Jamie-Lee Martin.

She had been nervous about the trip to Cranley Manor. Now she wanted to go home.

'Go and get your bags,' said Mrs Scott. 'I want you to settle in to your rooms.'

Najma looked at Kat and Loz. Maybe one of them would swap with her. But they both stared at the floor. They didn't want to share with Jamie-Lee, either.

Chapter 3

Najma unpacked quickly. She put her clothes in a drawer. Then she shoved her pyjamas under her pillow.

Jamie-Lee took a long time to unpack. She had brought too many clothes. She had things like face cream, shampoo and scent, and loads of sweets and chocolate.

Then she unpacked a Walkman and six tapes. These were forbidden on the trip. She hid the Walkman in her drawer.

Jamie-Lee looked at Najma. 'Don't you dare tell,' she said.

Emma and Lucy didn't say much to Najma. They pulled their beds next to Jamie-Lee's. 'The three of us can be together,' said Lucy.

Najma said nothing. She went to find Kat and Loz.

Chapter 4

Cranley Manor was close to the sea. Schools used it all the time for trips. It was a rambling old house. The rooms at the front were very grand. Schools didn't use these. They used the rooms at the back.

Most rooms were quite plain and shabby. There was a dining room with long tables. There was a classroom and a games room. The bedrooms were upstairs on two floors.

Najma looked for Kat and Loz. Their room was number 12. Najma couldn't see it on her floor. Maybe it was on the next floor.

The trouble was, Najma couldn't find the stairs. She must have taken a wrong turning. 'I can't be lost,' she sighed.

Then she came to a steep staircase with a door at the top. 'Maybe this is the way,' she thought. She climbed the stairs and pushed the door open.

She found herself in a long, narrow corridor. It was gloomy and it smelled musty. At first Najma found it hard to see. The corridor was quite dark with no windows. 'This can't be right,' she thought.

Suddenly Najma stopped. Someone was at the end of the corridor. The hair at the back of Najma's neck tingled. Her skin felt cold.

Najma saw the figure of a young girl wearing a long blue cloak. She appeared only for a second. Then she was gone.

'Oh no!' breathed Najma. Her heart was thumping and her mouth felt dry. 'That was the girl I saw in the picture. I've seen a ghost.'

Chapter 5

Najma ran back down the stairs. Her mind was racing. 'I'm being silly,' she told herself. 'How can I have seen a ghost? There are no such things. It was just my imagination.'

She decided to say nothing. Not even to Loz and Kat.

She met Mrs Scott outside her room.

'Are you all right, Najma?' asked Mrs Scott. 'You look pale.'

'Yes, I'm fine,' said Najma. 'I feel a bit homesick, that's all.'

'You'll feel fine once we start doing things,' said Mrs Scott. She called everyone out of their rooms.

'I want everyone downstairs,' said Mrs Scott. 'Put on outdoor shoes and a warm sweater. There's time for an activity before supper.'

'What are we going to do?' asked Emma.

'We're going for a walk,' said Mrs Scott.

'Do we have to?' complained Jamie-Lee.

'Don't start moaning,' said Mrs Scott. 'The walk will be exciting.'

The walk was exciting. But not in the way Mrs Scott meant.

Chapter 6

Najma was glad to go for a walk.
She met up with Kat and Loz. Chris,
Andy and Gizmo joined them. Gizmo
was grinning. 'This is a great place,'
he said. 'Has your room got bunk
beds? Ours has.'

Mr Saffrey pointed to a hill behind
the manor house. 'We're going to
climb that hill,' he said. 'There's a
surprise at the top.'

'Then we'll come back through the woods over there,' said Mrs Scott.

They set off up the hill. Everyone walked quickly. 'Slow down,' called Mr Saffrey. 'This isn't a race.'

Najma couldn't stop thinking about the girl in the blue cloak. At last she said, 'Do you think the house is haunted?'

Kat laughed. 'No!' she said. 'There are no such things as ghosts.'

Gizmo told a joke, 'What do short-sighted ghosts wear?' he asked.

Nobody answered.

At last they reached the very top of the hill. Then they saw it. The sea. It foamed through an archway in a huge rock. Curving away into the mist was a line of cliffs. Yellow gorse grew on the cliff top. Gulls flew in circles overhead.

Andy gasped. 'What a sight!' he said.

'It's amazing,' said Najma. 'What a pity it's so misty. I bet you can see for miles on a clear day.'

'Spook-tacles,' said Gizmo. But nobody was listening.

Chapter 7

A cool wind blew in from the sea. It brought the mist with it. It began to blot out the view. Everyone began to feel cold.

'Time to go back,' said Mrs Scott. She set off along the path through the woods. 'Come along, everyone,' she called. 'Keep in a group.'

The path was narrow. Najma and Andy walked together. They were behind everyone else. Then Najma had to stop. Her shoelace had come undone. 'Bother,' she said. 'The lace has broken.'

The mist grew thicker. It felt like a clammy white blanket. It seemed to taste of the sea.

Andy sounded scared. 'Come on, Najma, let's catch up with the others.'

They went as fast as they could, but it was hard to see the way. They came to a fork in the path. 'I don't like this,' said Andy. 'Which way do we go?'

They took the path on the left. Soon it turned sharply and began to go up hill again. 'This can't be right,' said Najma.

Then they both stopped. A little
way ahead was a figure. They could
just see her through the mist.

Najma went icy cold all over. She
grabbed Andy's arm. It was the girl
in the blue cloak. She was pointing
back down the path. 'It's a ghost,'
gasped Najma. 'Run, Andy.'

They scrambled back the way they
had come. Then they heard Mr
Saffrey calling them. He was waiting
at the fork.

'Thank goodness,' he said. 'We
thought you were lost.'

Chapter 8

Najma and Andy told Kat about the girl they had seen on the path.

'She can't have been a ghost,' said Andy. 'She didn't spook us. She was just pointing.'

'Well why did you both run away, then?' asked Kat.

'It was because Najma was so scared,' said Andy. 'It scared me.'

'This place can't be haunted,' said Kat. 'It's used all the time by schools.'

'But I've seen the girl twice,' said Najma. 'I saw her in a corridor.'

'Who is this girl, anyway?' asked Andy.

'She's in a picture,' said Najma. 'Why don't we ask Mrs Scott about her?'

So that evening, they asked about the girl in blue. 'Why does she look so unhappy?' asked Najma.

'It's a sad story,' said Mrs Scott. 'She's called Amy. Her father was Lord Cranley. He had to go to war. He told Amy he would soon be back. "I'll bring you a present," he told her.

'Day after day, Amy waited. The weeks went by. Then came terrible news. Amy's father had been killed.

'But he had kept his promise. In the saddle pack of his horse was a present for Amy. It was a blue velvet cloak.

'After that Amy always wore the blue cloak. One day, she became very ill. But she wouldn't take off the cloak, even though she was so ill. Soon after that, she died.'

Najma didn't say anything. But now she felt sure she had seen the ghost of Amy Cranley.

Chapter 9

Najma didn't sleep very well that night. Jamie-Lee, Emma and Lucy talked for a long time.

Jamie-Lee went to sleep with her Walkman on. Najma could hear it playing in the darkness. *'Tchk, tchk, tchk-tchk. Tchk, tchk-tchk,'* it went.

Najma put her head under the pillow. At last she fell asleep. She thought she might dream of the girl in blue, but she didn't.

By the morning, the sea mist had gone. The sky was clear and bright. After breakfast, they all worked in the classroom.

Mrs Scott talked about the sea shore. 'This afternoon we're going to study the beach and look at rock pools,' she said. 'I want you to work in groups of six.'

Mrs Scott told them who was in each group.

Mrs Scott put Najma with Jamie-Lee and Lucy. The boys in the group were Andy, Chris and Michael Ward.

Nobody was happy with the groups. Kat put up her hand. 'Please, Mrs Scott,' she said. 'Last year, we always worked with our friends.'

Mrs Scott smiled. 'I know,' she said. 'But I'd like you to try a new group today. It's not good to be in the same group all the time.'

Kat didn't agree, but she kept quiet.

Chapter 10

The beach study was good fun.
First, they looked for shells along the
tide line. Mrs Scott told them the
names of unusual shells.

Next, they did a rock pool search.
Michael Ward was good at finding
things. He and Andy lifted big stones
and seaweed. Underneath they found
green crabs and shrimps.

Everyone liked looking in the rock
pools. They looked at sea anemones
and dipped for rock guppies.

The tide was coming in. Mrs
Scott told them to go to the top of
the beach. 'Who can find a lucky
stone with a hole in it?' she called.

Everyone began to search among
the shingle. There were plenty of
unusual pebbles but it was hard to
find one with a hole.

Najma's group came to the end of the beach. On the other side of a rocky cliff was a little cove.

They began to explore the rocks below the cliff. 'Come on,' said Jamie-Lee. 'Let's go into the next cove.'

'We were told not to,' said Andy.

'Oh, come on,' said Lucy. 'We won't be long. We may be lucky and find a stone with a hole in it.'

So they made their way round the end of the cliff.

'We'd better be quick,' said Najma. 'The tide's coming in fast.'

Chapter 11

The cove was quite small. It had no sand – only rocks and shingle. Above it, the cliff rose up steeply.

Everyone began to search for a stone with a hole in it. There was a small cave at the back of the cove. Chris and Najma ran to look there. The others joined them.

The cave was damp and clammy. 'The tide comes right in here,' said Michael Ward.

'We ought to go back,' said Andy.

They made their way back to the edge of the cove. But they were too late. The sea was swirling round the rocks.

It was amazing how fast the tide had come in. Already it was about two metres in from the end.

'Oh no!' cried Lucy. 'We're cut off.'

Everyone felt a sense of panic. They knew they were in danger. The sea came right in to the cove. All round them the cliffs rose like steep walls.

'We shouldn't have come,' said Lucy.

'Maybe we can wade back round,' said Jamie-Lee. She pulled off her trainers and socks. Everyone did the same.

They started wading, but the rocks were uneven. Soon the water came up to their thighs. 'It's too deep,' said Andy. 'Go back! I don't think we can get round.'

A big wave came in suddenly. Just then, Lucy slipped. The sea washed her forward, then it sucked her back.

Lucy thrashed about in the water. 'Help!' she shouted.

Chapter 12

For a few seconds everyone stared in horror. Lucy struggled to get up, but a wave knocked her over again.

Najma acted. 'Form a chain,' she shouted. Then she grabbed Andy's hand.

The others linked up. Najma inched her way towards Lucy. She gasped as a wave hit her in the stomach. 'Don't let go,' she yelled at the others.

Then she grabbed Lucy's hand and pulled her up. 'Well done,' gasped Andy.

Everyone waded out of the sea.
Everyone was wet, but Najma and
Lucy were soaked. Lucy was crying.

'What are we going to do?' said
Michael Ward. 'We've got to get out
of here. If we don't, we'll drown.'

Lucy and Najma were already
feeling chilled. Their wet clothes felt
heavy and cold.

'Someone will rescue us,' said Chris. 'Surely the coast guard will come?'

Lucy and Najma began to shiver. 'You must not get too cold,' said Andy. He pulled off his sweater. He made Chris do the same. 'Put these on,' he said.

Najma was glad to get out of her wet top and put Andy's sweater on.

'We'll need a safe place to shelter,' she said. 'The sea will come right into the cove.'

Najma looked at the cliff. Then she stared in amazement. Standing on a ledge, just above them, was the girl in blue.

'It's the ghost,' said Najma.

Chapter 13

Slowly the ghost began to move.
She made her way along the ledge.
Then she climbed down towards the
cove.

'It's that girl, again,' said Andy.
'The one you thought was a ghost.'

Soon the girl was just above them. She jumped down the last few feet on to the shingle.

'So you've been cut off by the tide,' she said.

Najma looked at her. She didn't look anything like a ghost. In fact she was an ordinary, normal girl.

'I live in the Manor,' she said. 'That's where you're staying. My mum is the Warden.'

'I thought you were a ghost,' said Najma. 'You look like Amy Cranley.'

The girl laughed. 'I know I do. I like playing tricks. Sometimes I pretend I'm a ghost. It's a good joke.'

'I'm sorry, but I don't think so,' said Najma.

'How did you get down here?' asked Jamie-Lee.

'There's a secret way,' said the girl. 'Years ago some smugglers cut steps up the cliff. You can't see them from the cove. Not many people know about them.'

The girl made them climb up to a ledge. 'We must go up in stages. I'll lead you up one at a time. You'll be quite safe, but don't look down.'

So, one by one, everyone climbed up the cliff. As they got to the top, there was a bang and a puff of smoke in the sky.

'That's the signal for the lifeboat. Someone's called it out,' said the girl.

'Well, we're going to be in trouble,' said Chris.

Chapter 14

They all felt much better at the top of the cliff. They looked back to the cove. It looked a long way down.

Chris wiped his forehead. He looked for the smugglers' steps. It was impossible to see where they were.

The tide had moved into the cove.
It had reached the bottom of the cliff.
The sea was beating around the
rocks where Lucy fell in.

'Phew!' said Michael Ward. 'I'm
glad we got out of there.'

Chris looked at the girl. 'Yes, thanks
for rescuing us,' he said. 'But how did
you know we'd been cut off by the
tide?'

The girl grinned. 'I was watching you from the top.'

'We'd better get back to the beach,' said Lucy. 'I must tell Mrs Scott that we're safe.'

They began to walk down the cliff path.

Najma hung back. She wanted to talk to the girl. 'I'm sure I saw you in the house,' she said. 'Then Andy and I saw you in the wood. It was when that sea mist came down.'

The girl didn't say anything.

'But why do you wear a blue cloak?' asked Najma.

The girl smiled. 'I told you,' she said. 'I like playing tricks.'

They had almost reached the beach. They could see Mrs Scott striding towards them.

She was looking very serious.

They all began to run towards her. Najma looked back at the girl. 'By the way,' she called. 'What's your name?'

'Amy,' the girl replied.

Chapter 15

They were in serious trouble. Mr Saffrey was very cross. 'I'm thinking of sending you home,' he told them.

'You were told not to go into the cove,' he said. 'It was silly and dangerous. Think what might have happened. If you hadn't got up the cliff, you might have drowned.'

Mrs Scott frowned. 'I can't imagine how you got up the cliff,' she said.

'This girl showed us the way,' said Chris. 'We used the smugglers' steps.'

'I've never heard of smugglers' steps,' said Mrs Scott. 'And who was this girl?'

'She lives here,' said Najma. 'She's the Warden's daughter. She played a trick on me and Andy. Her name is Amy.'

'Well, the Warden *does* have a daughter,' said Mrs Scott. 'But her name isn't Amy . . . it's Jenny.'

Level 1

The Hole in the Ground
Hidden Gold
The Flying Armchair
I Hate Computers!
The Night it Rained Chips
Toxic Waste

More Level 1

People Like That
Andy the Hero
Fair Scare
It Can't Be
Blaze!
A Good Tip

Level 2

Funny Sort of Treasure
Arjo's Bike
In the Net
Million-Dollar Egg
The Exploding Parrot
The Pool Party

Level 3

Siren Green
Remote Control
Blazing Burgers
Skydive Wedding
Electric Sandwiches
The Copper Cockerel

Level 4

Who's Kooza?
Ghost
In the End
Let's Hear It for Nan
Hostage!
Dirt Bike Rider

Level 5

Black Holme Island
Who Kidnapped the Mayor?
Scottish Adventure
Alien
Sleepover Shock
Last Term at Wolf Hill